primer level

TECHNIC LESSONS

by JAMES BASTIEN

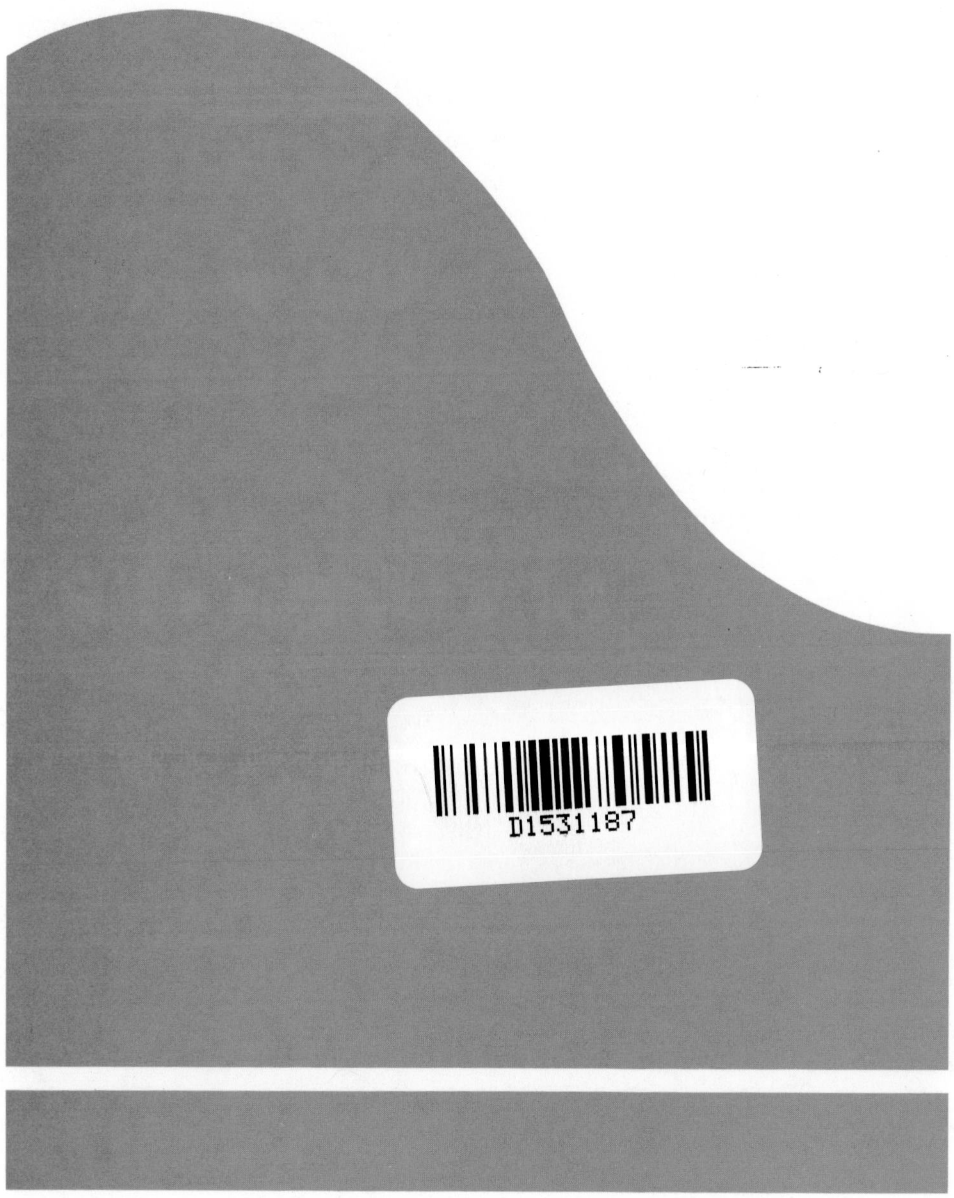

D1531187

KJOS WEST · Neil A. Kjos, Jr. Publisher · San Diego, California

TO THE TEACHER

TECHNIC LESSONS, Primer Level, is designed to be used simultaneously with **PIANO LESSONS, Primer Level,** by UNITS. *(© 1976 Kjos West, San Diego, California. Ed. No. WP1)* It may also be used with any other piano course.

DYNAMICS Dynamics are not introduced until UNIT 6 (page 19). However, dynamic suggestions may be given prior to that time at the teacher's discretion.

TEMPO Because these exercises are designed for the beginner, the student will play at his own tempo in the beginning. Later, the teacher can encourage the student to play each exercise in three tempos: slow, medium and fast. Have the student repeat each exercise using a different tempo each time.

TOUCH Staccato touch is not introduced until UNIT 6 (page 22). The basic touch for these exercises is legato. However, some of the exercises may be repeated played staccato at the teacher's discretion.

The materials at the beginning of this book (pages 6 - 11) may be taught by rote. The *Teacher's Notes* at the bottom of these pages show alternate fingerings and give suggestions for practicing the patterns up or down the keyboard.

The goal of **TECHNIC LESSONS** is to develop hand and finger coordination and facility, and to develop ease and control at the keyboard. A variety of keyboard experiences is provided to give the student a basic foundation in beginning fundamentals.

Suggested Use of Materials with "PIANO LESSONS, Primer Level"

At the **first lesson** the student may be given .... **Music Notebook** (GP16)
After completing **page 6**, the student is ready to begin .... **Theory Lessons**—Primer Level (WP6)
After completing **page 13**, the student is ready to begin .... **Technic Lessons**—Primer Level (WP11)
After completing **page 25**, the student is ready to begin .... **Piano Solos**—Primer Level (WP22)
After completing **page 33**, the student is ready to begin .... **Music Flashcards** (GP27)
After completing **page 56**, the student is ready to begin
these Supplementary Books .... **Christmas Favorites**—Primer Level (WP48)
Favorite Classic Melodies—Primer Level (WP72)
Folk Tune Favorites—Primer Level (WP46)
Hymn Favorites—Primer Level (WP43)
Piano Recital Solos—Primer Level (WP64)

SHEET MUSIC from **Primer Level Solos** may be assigned to the student at the teacher's discretion. (Begin sheet music with Unit 6.)

ISBN 0-8497-5010-5

Any reproduction, adaptation or arrangement of this work in whole or in part without the consent of the copyright owner constitutes an infringement of copyright.
© **1976 Kjos West, San Diego, California**
Inter. Copyright Secured All Rights Reserved Printed in U.S.A.

TO THE STUDENT

The studies in this book are designed to help you play the piano with ease and control. Allow time each day for technic practice. You might use these studies as warm-ups before beginning to practice your pieces.

Think of these three points often.

HEIGHT Sit up high enough to reach the keys easily. Your wrists and forearms should be in a *straight line* over the keys. Do you have a piano stool or a piano chair at home which moves up and down? If not, cushions or telephone books will help raise you up when you practice.

POSTURE Sit up *straight* in front of the center of the piano (by the piano's name). Place your feet flat on the floor. Do your feet reach the floor? If not, it is helpful to have a footstool under them when you practice.

HAND POSITION When playing the piano, hold your fingers in a nice *curved shape*. Imagine you are holding a ball. This is the way the fingers should be curved when playing the piano.

CONTENTS

10-14-93

UNIT 1

PLAYING CLUSTERS

OFF WE GO!

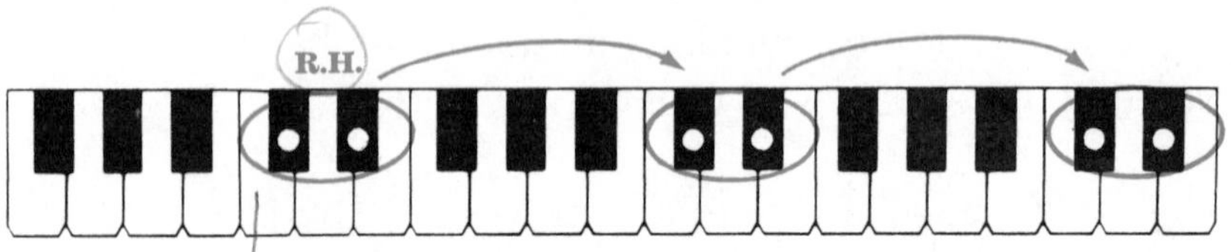
R.H.
middle

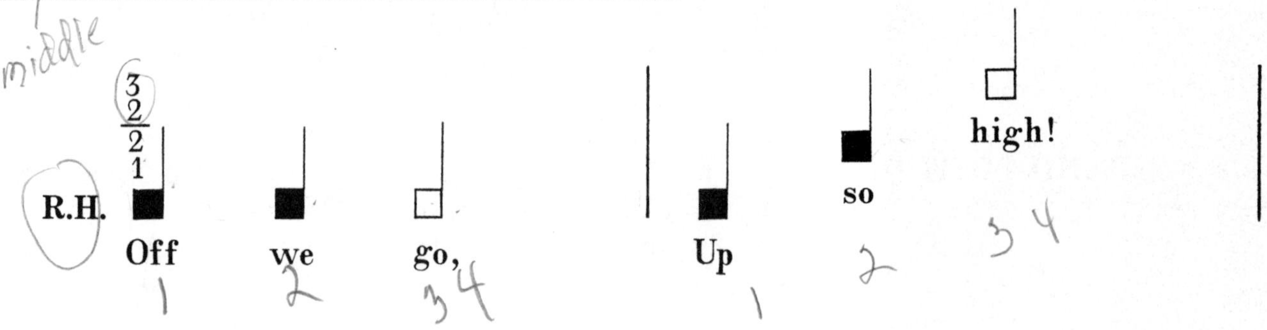
R.H.
3
2
2
1
Off
we
go,
Up
so
high!

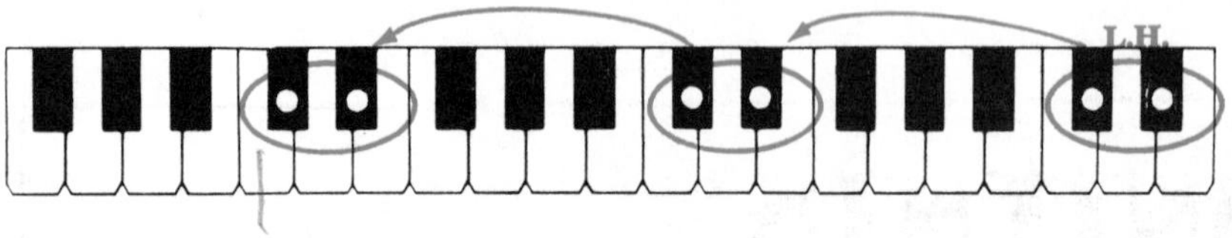
L.H.

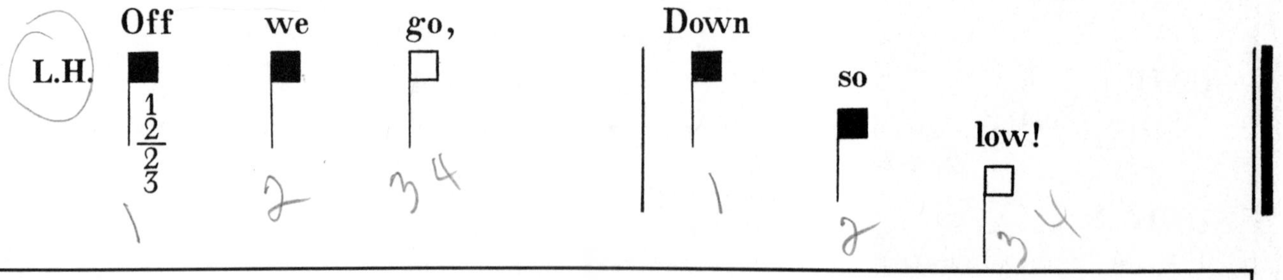
L.H.
Off
we
go,
Down
so
low!
1
2
2
3

Teacher's Notes

Any reproduction, adaptation or arrangement of this work in whole or in part without the consent of the copyright owner constitutes an infringement of copyright.
© 1976 Kjos West, San Diego, California
Inter. Copyright Secured All Rights Reserved Printed in U.S.A.

10-21-93

THE 747 JET

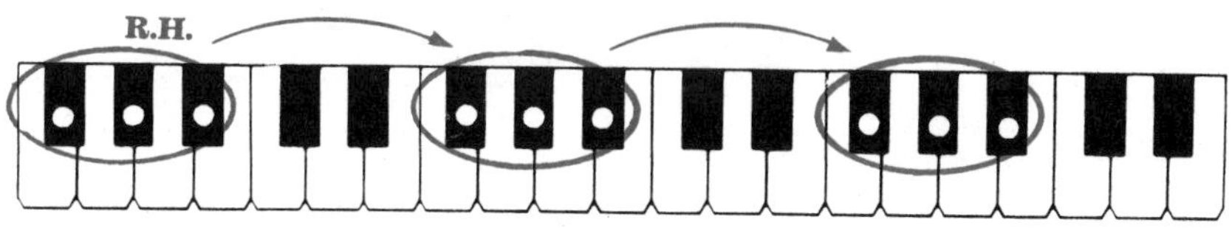
R.H.

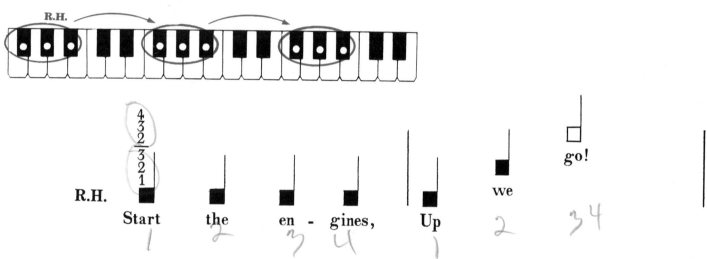

R.H. Start the en - gines, Up we go!

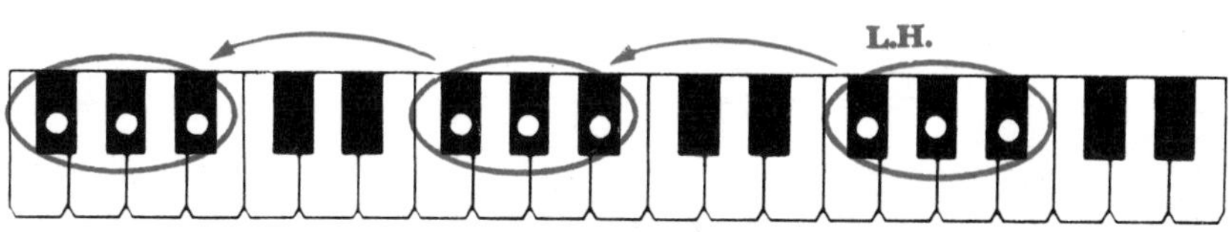
L.H.

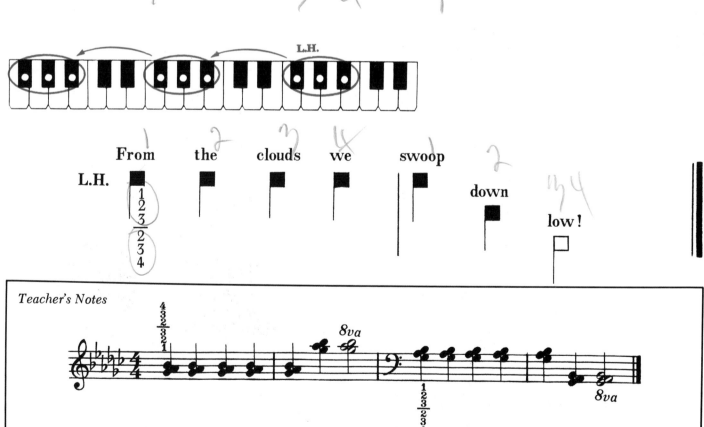

L.H. From the clouds we swoop down low!

Teacher's Notes

8va
8va

10-28-93

UNIT 2

PLAYING 2NDS

LEGATO

THE SEESAW

Play 2nds up the keyboard.

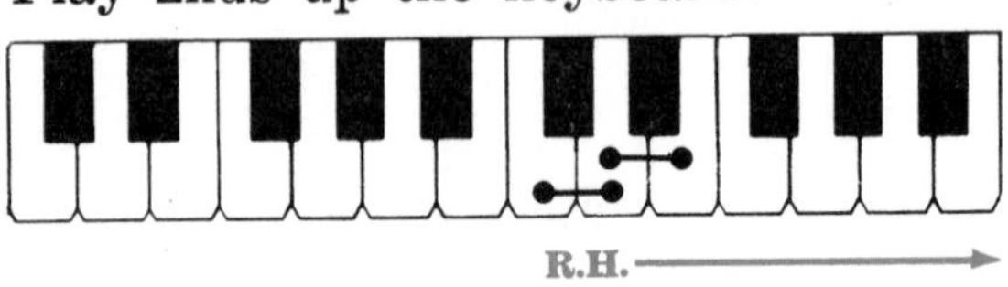
R.H.

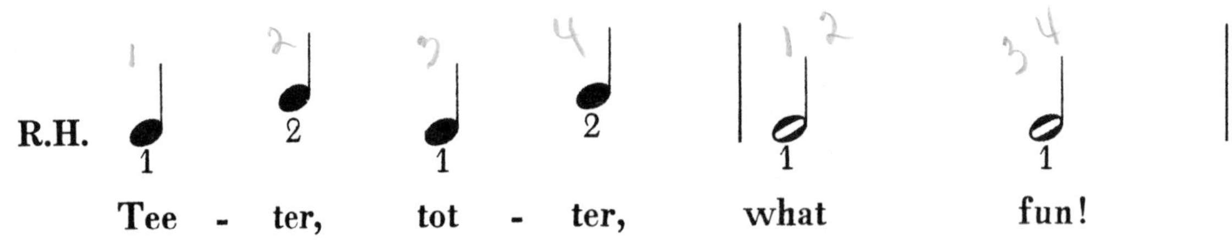
R.H.
1 2 1 2 1 1
Tee - ter, tot - ter, what fun!

Play 2nds down the keyboard.

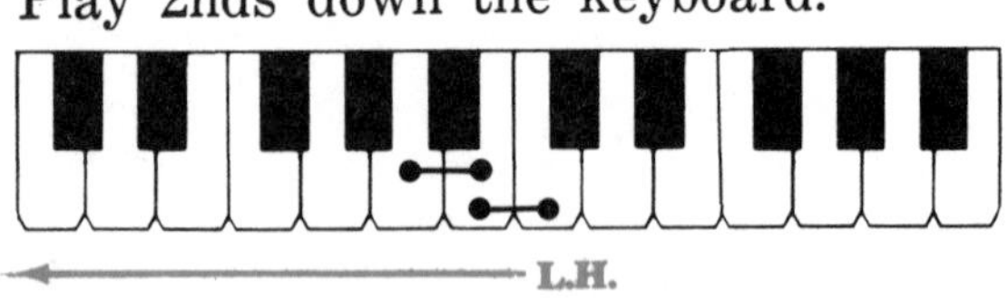
L.H.

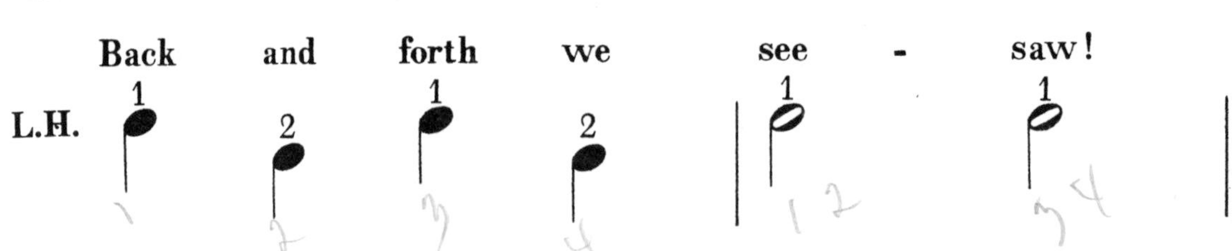
Back and forth we see - saw!
L.H.
1 2 1 2 1 1

Teacher's Notes

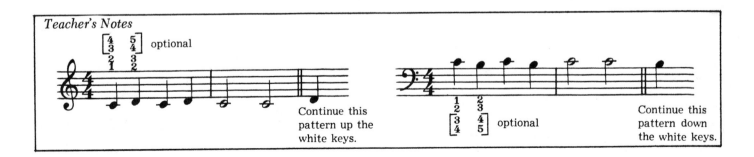

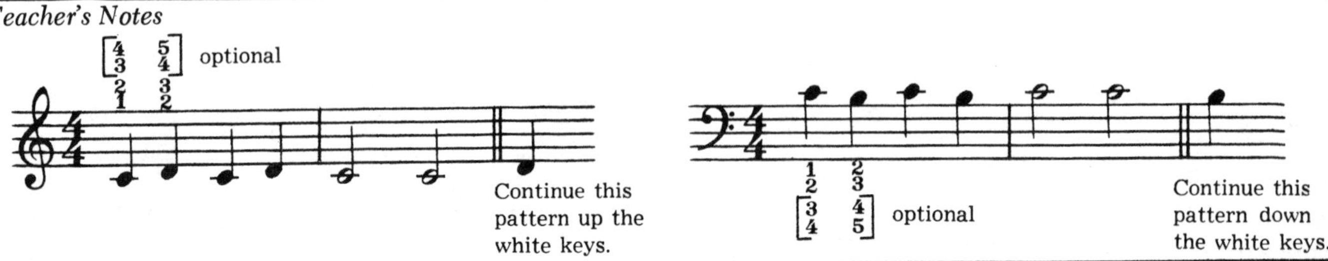
optional
Continue this pattern up the white keys.
optional
Continue this pattern down the white keys.

PLAYING 3RDS
LEGATO

CHURCH BELLS

Play 3rds up the keyboard.

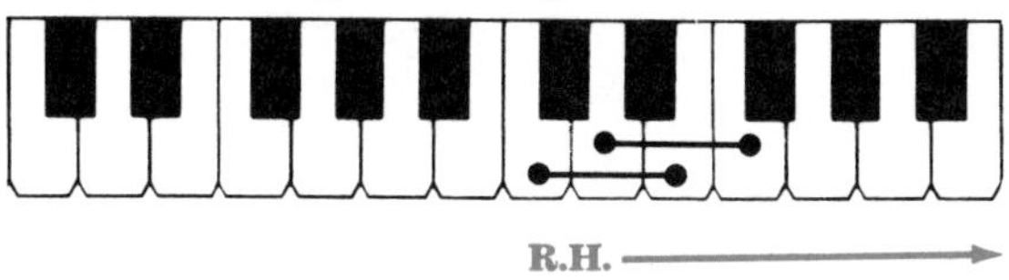
R.H.

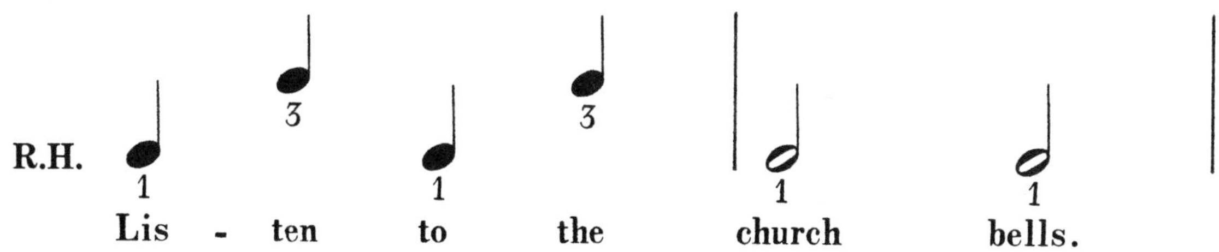
R.H.
1 3 1 3 1 1
Lis - ten to the church bells.

Play 3rds down the keyboard.

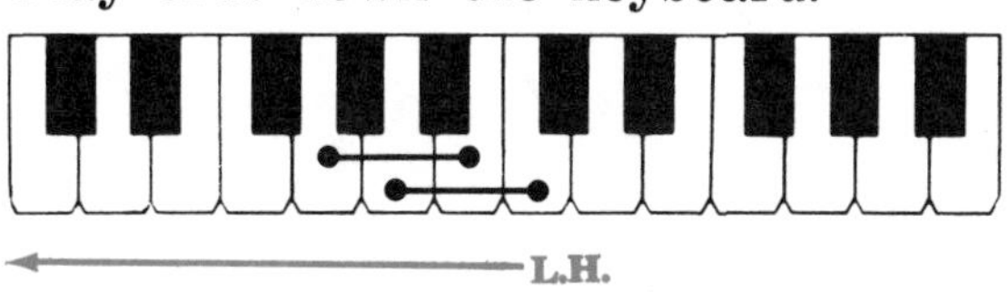
L.H.

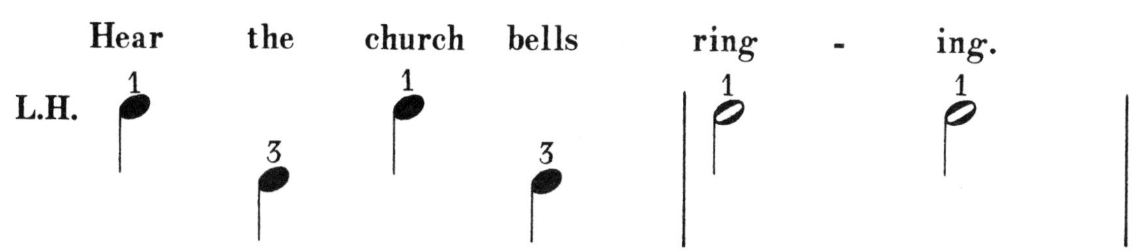
Hear the church bells ring - ing.
L.H.
1 3 1 3 1 1

Teacher's Notes

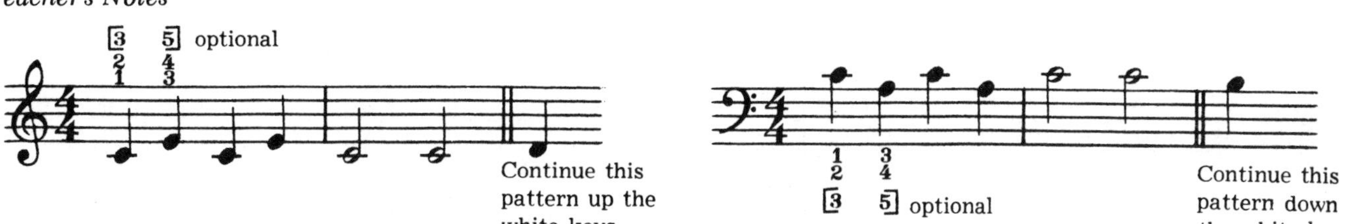
3 5 optional
2 4
1 3
Continue this pattern up the white keys.
1 3
2 4
3 5 optional
Continue this pattern down the white keys.

C MAJOR FIVE FINGER POSITION

SLEDDING

Play Five Finger Positions up the keyboard. Begin with C Major.

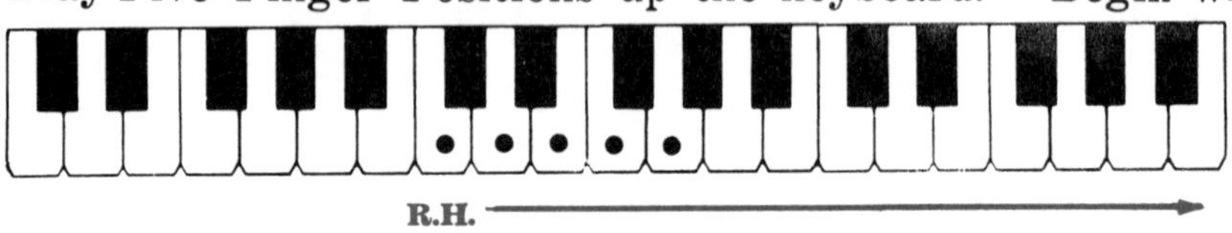
R.H.

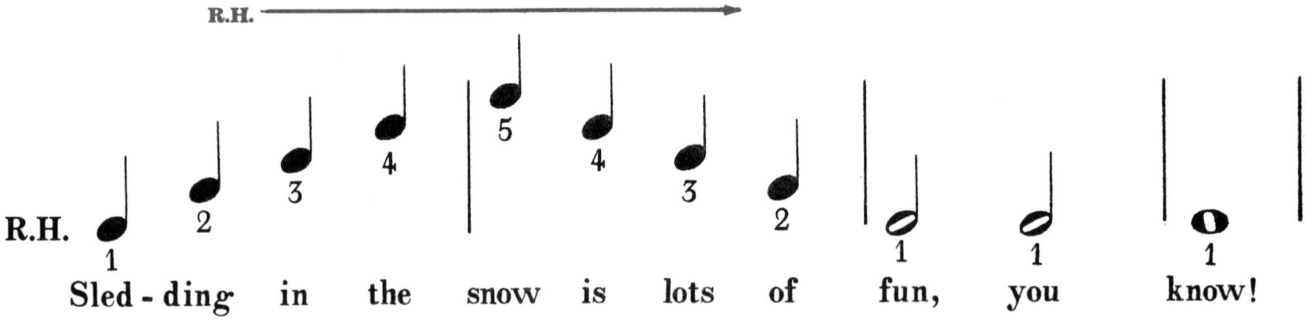
R.H.
1 2 3 4 5 4 3 2 1 1 1
Sled - ding in the snow is lots of fun, you know!

Play C Major Five Finger Positions up the keyboard.

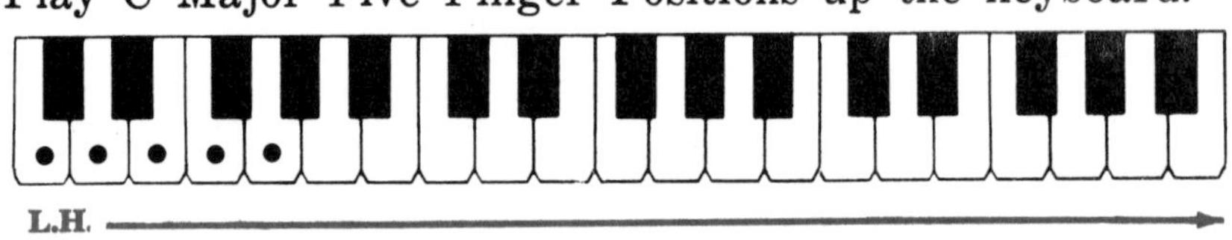
L.H.

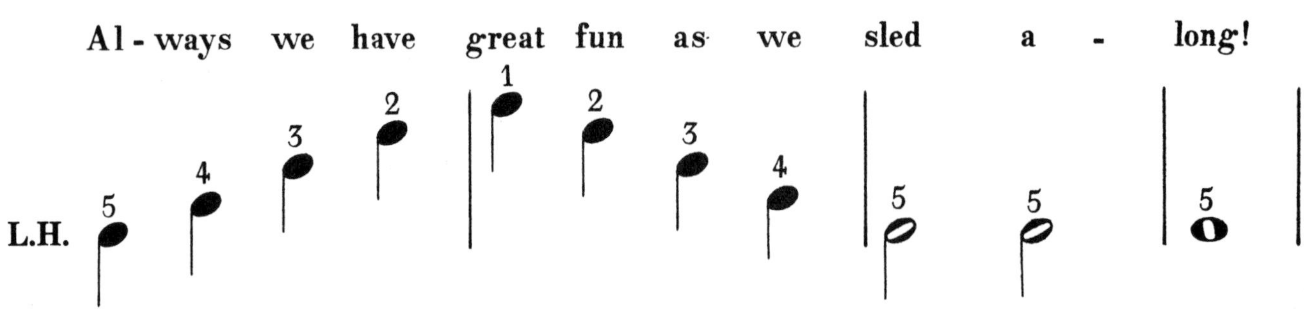
Al - ways we have great fun as we sled a - long!
L.H.
5 4 3 2 1 2 3 4 5 5 5

Teacher's Notes

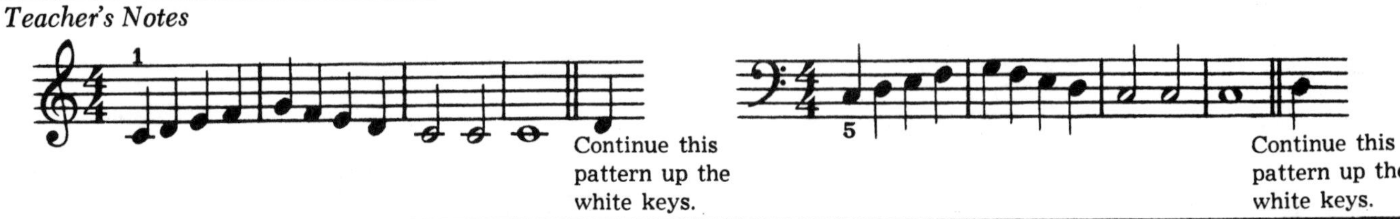
1
Continue this pattern up the white keys.
5
Continue this pattern up the white keys.

UNIT 3

PLAYING 2NDS

LEGATO

TAKING STEPS

Play this pattern up the keyboard.

R.H.

R.H.

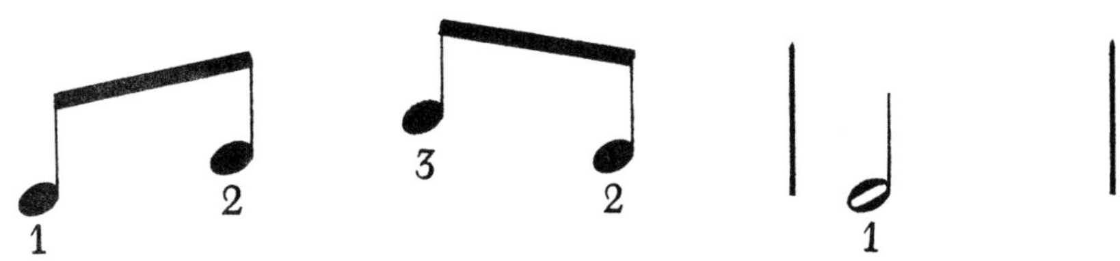
1
2
3
2
1

Step - ping up and down.

Play this pattern up the keyboard.

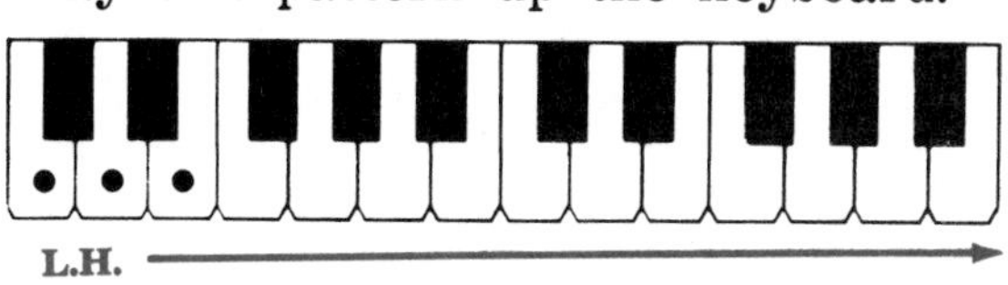
L.H.

Step - ping up and down.

L.H.

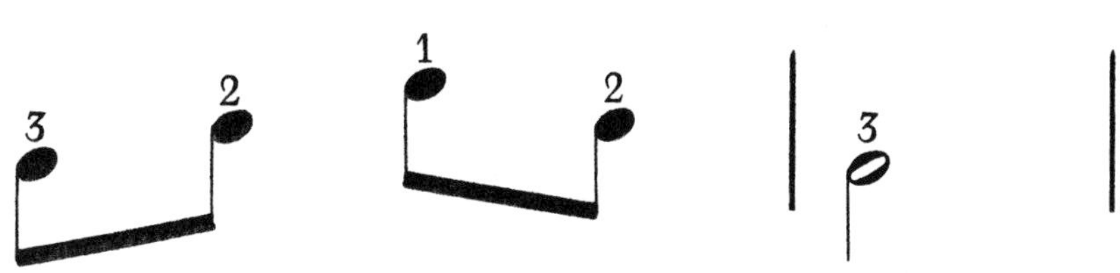
3
2
1
2
3

Teacher's Notes

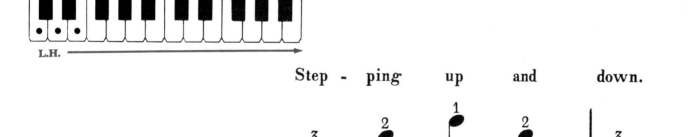

[3 4 5] optional
2 3 4
1 2 3

Continue this pattern up the white keys.

3 2 1
4 3 2
[5 4 3] optional

Continue this pattern up the white keys.

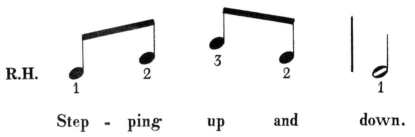

PLAYING 3RDS
LEGATO

TAKING SKIPS

Play 3rds up the keyboard.

R.H.

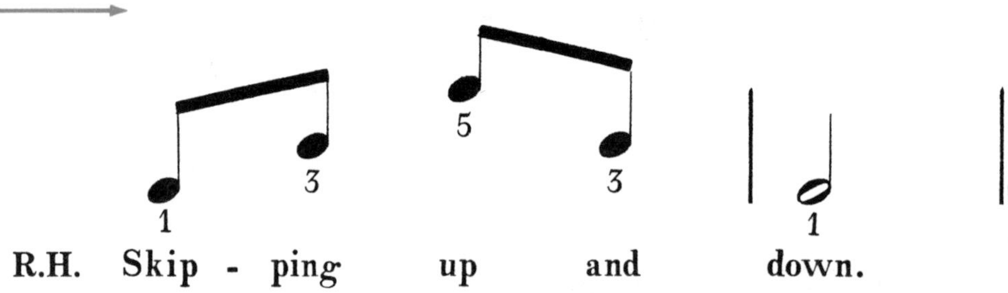
1
3
5
3
1
R.H. Skip - ping up and down.

Play 3rds up the keyboard.

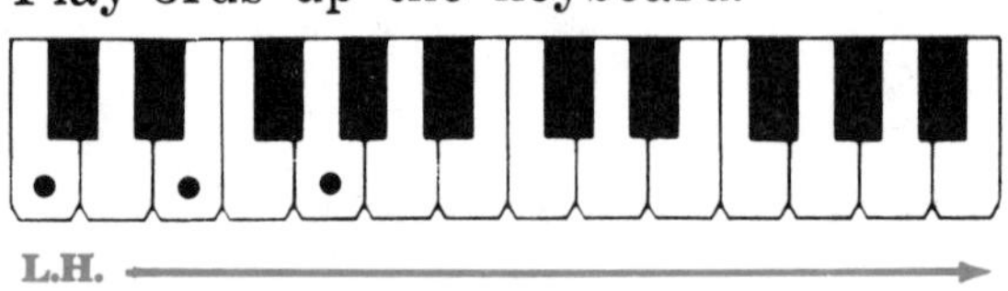
L.H.

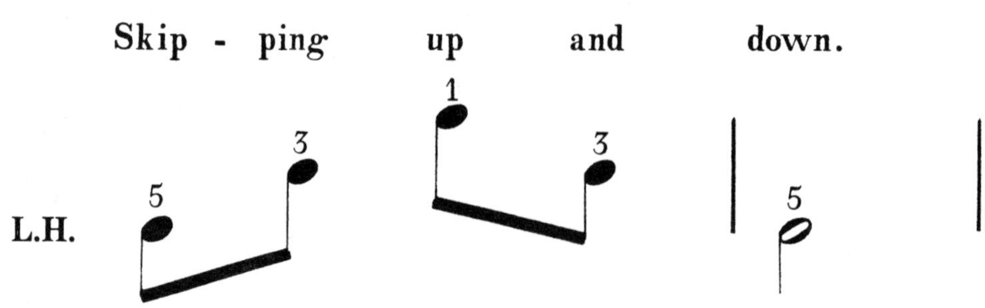
Skip - ping up and down.
5
3
1
3
5
L.H.

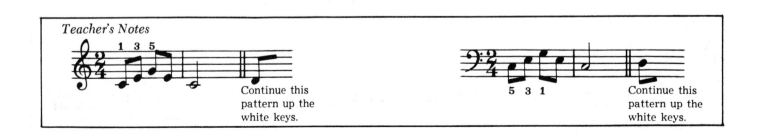

Teacher's Notes

1 3 5

Continue this pattern up the white keys.

5 3 1

Continue this pattern up the white keys.

PLAYING CHORDS

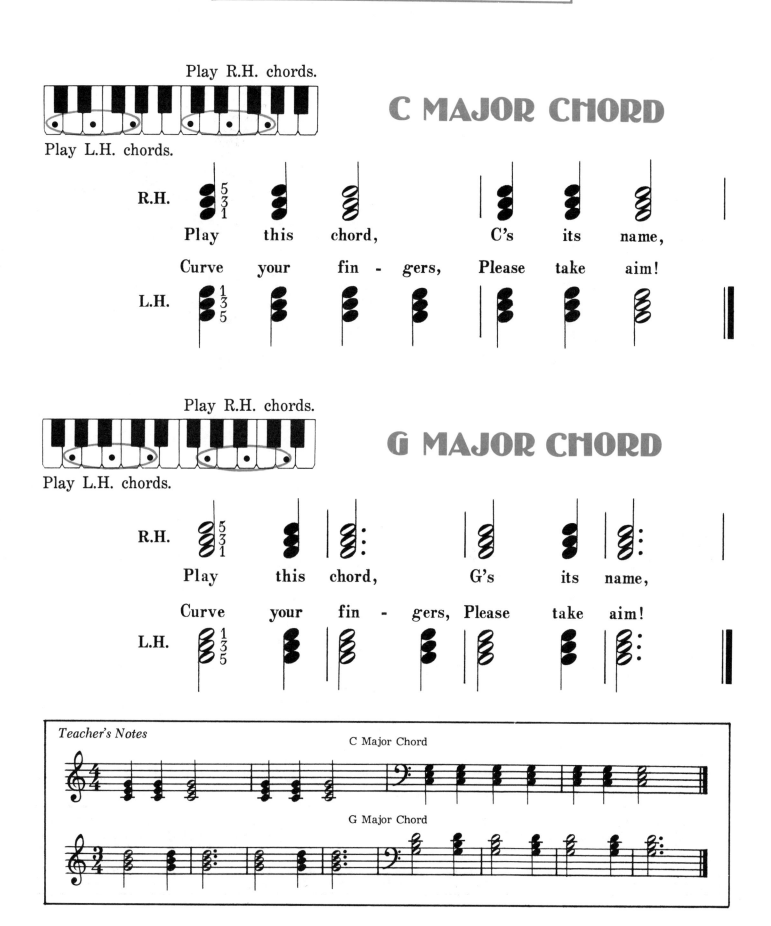

C MAJOR CHORD

Play R.H. chords.

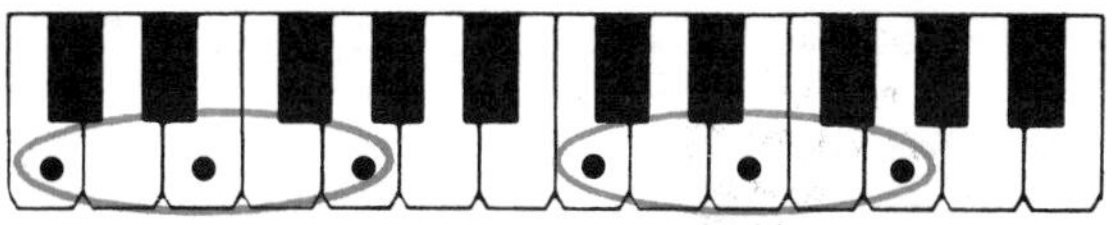

Play L.H. chords.

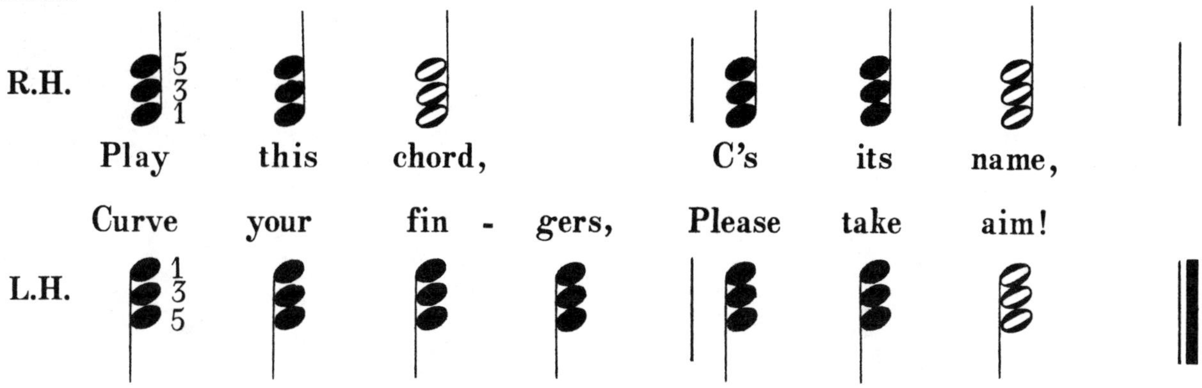
R.H.
5 3 1
Play this chord, C's its name,
Curve your fin - gers, Please take aim!
L.H.
1 3 5

G MAJOR CHORD

Play R.H. chords.

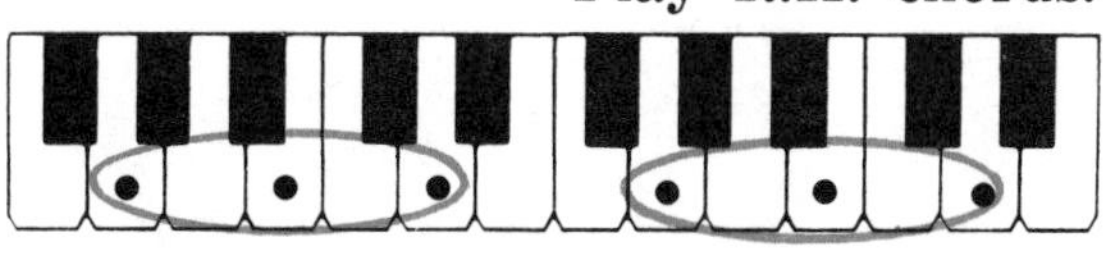

Play L.H. chords.

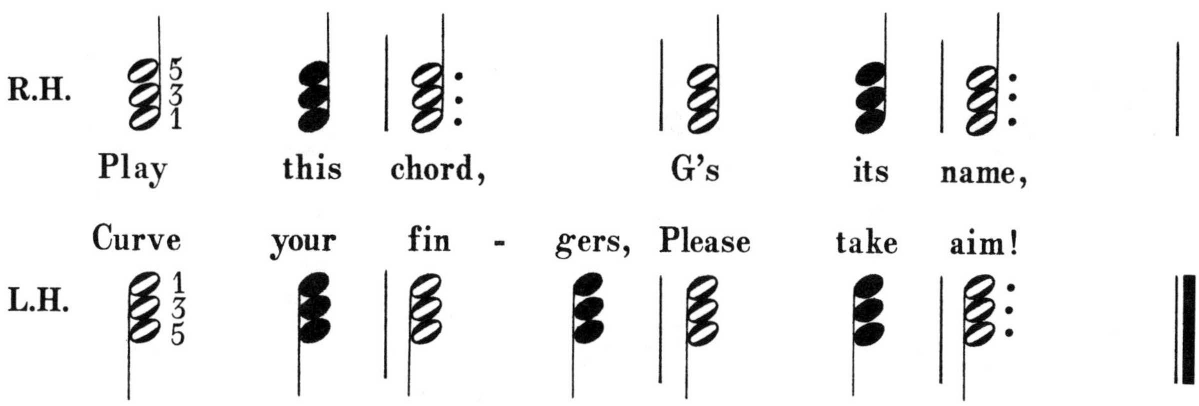
R.H.
5 3 1
Play this chord, G's its name,
Curve your fin - gers, Please take aim!
L.H.
1 3 5

Teacher's Notes

C Major Chord
G Major Chord

UNIT 4

G MAJOR FIVE FINGER POSITION

THE MIGHTY WATERFALL

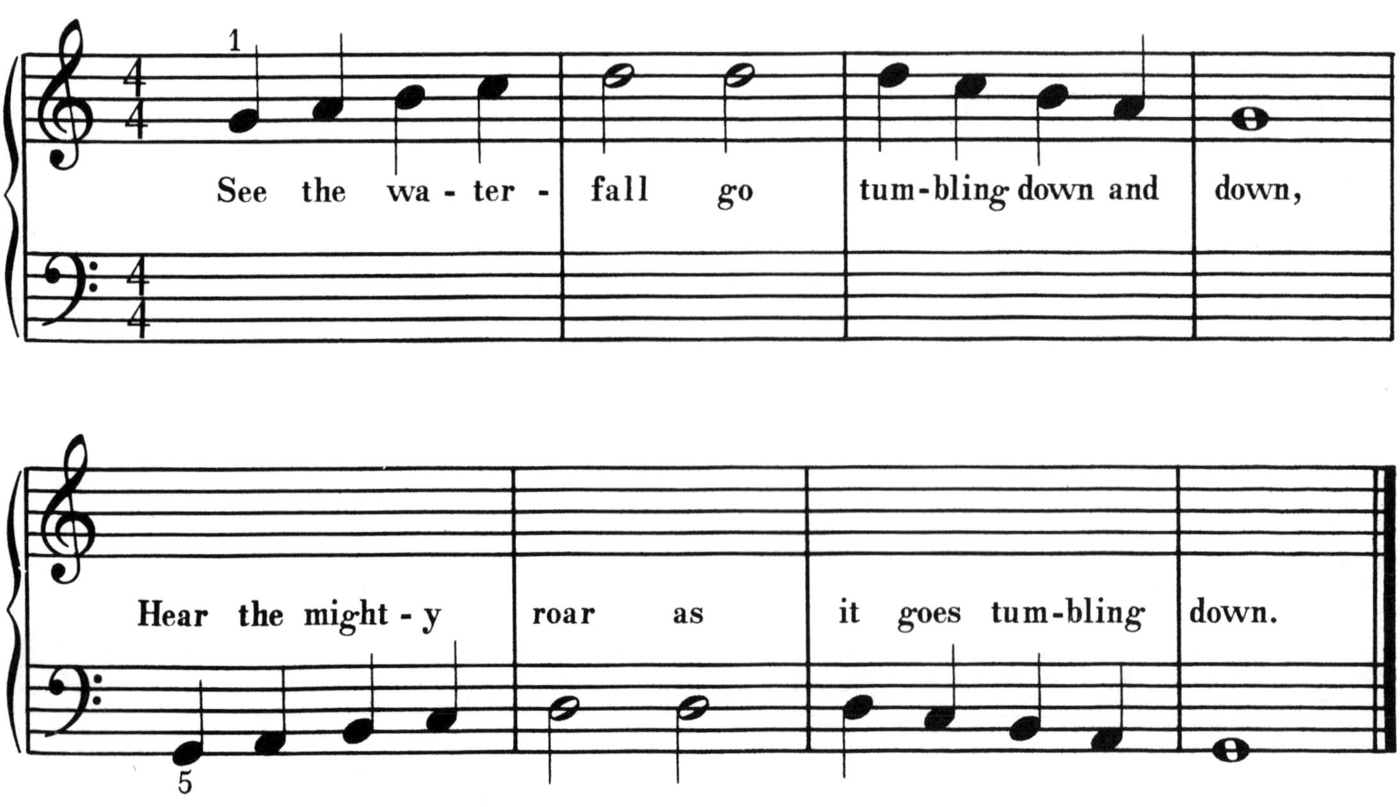
1
See the wa - ter - fall go tum-bling down and down,
Hear the might - y roar as it goes tum-bling down.
5

THE MEADOWLARK

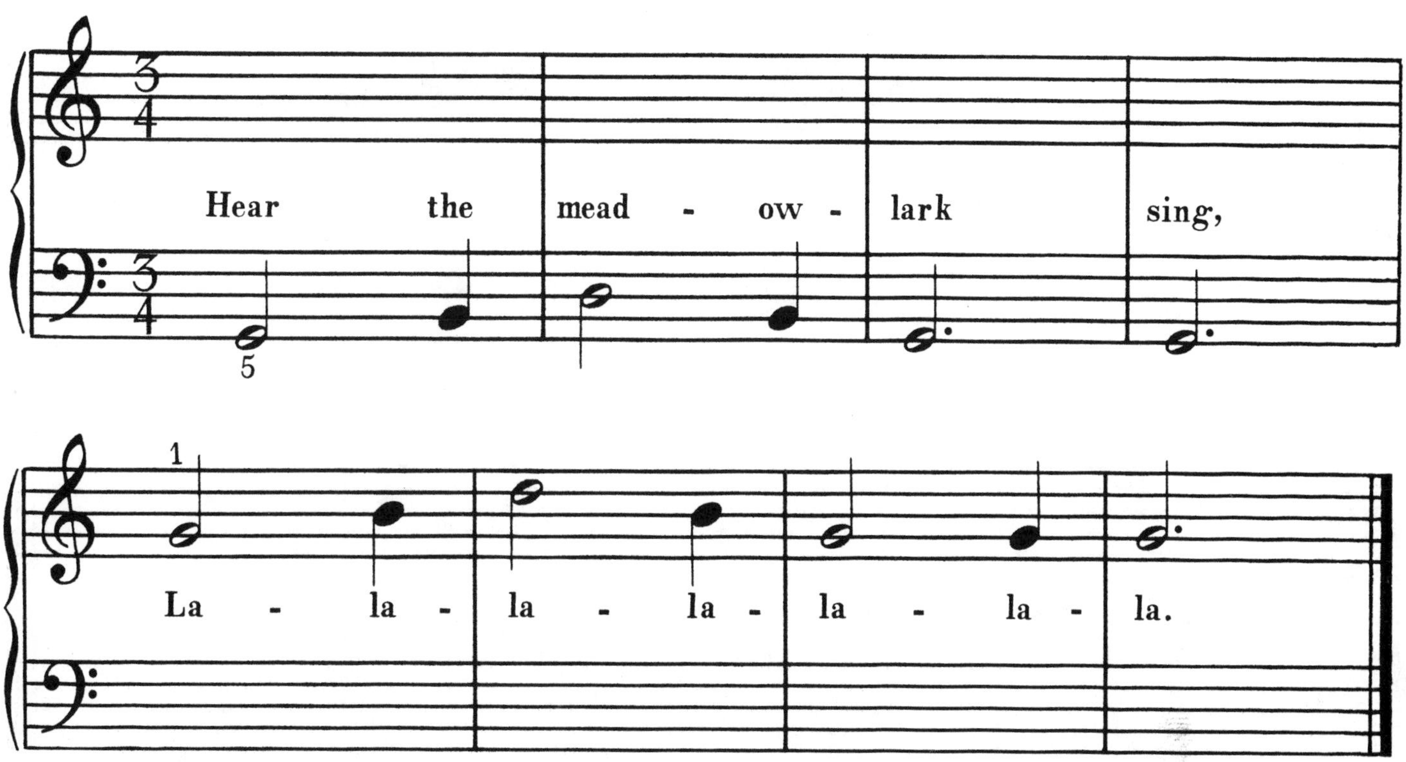
3/4
Hear the mead - ow - lark sing,
5
1
La - la - la - la - la - la - la.

DOLPHINS AT PLAY

SEAGULLS SWOOPING

UNIT 5

C MAJOR FIVE FINGER POSITION

THE FREIGHT TRAIN

1
4/4
See the smoke a - ris - ing, What a love - ly sight,
Watch the en - gine puff - ing, Pull - ing with its might!
5

PHRASING

CLOUDS FLOATING

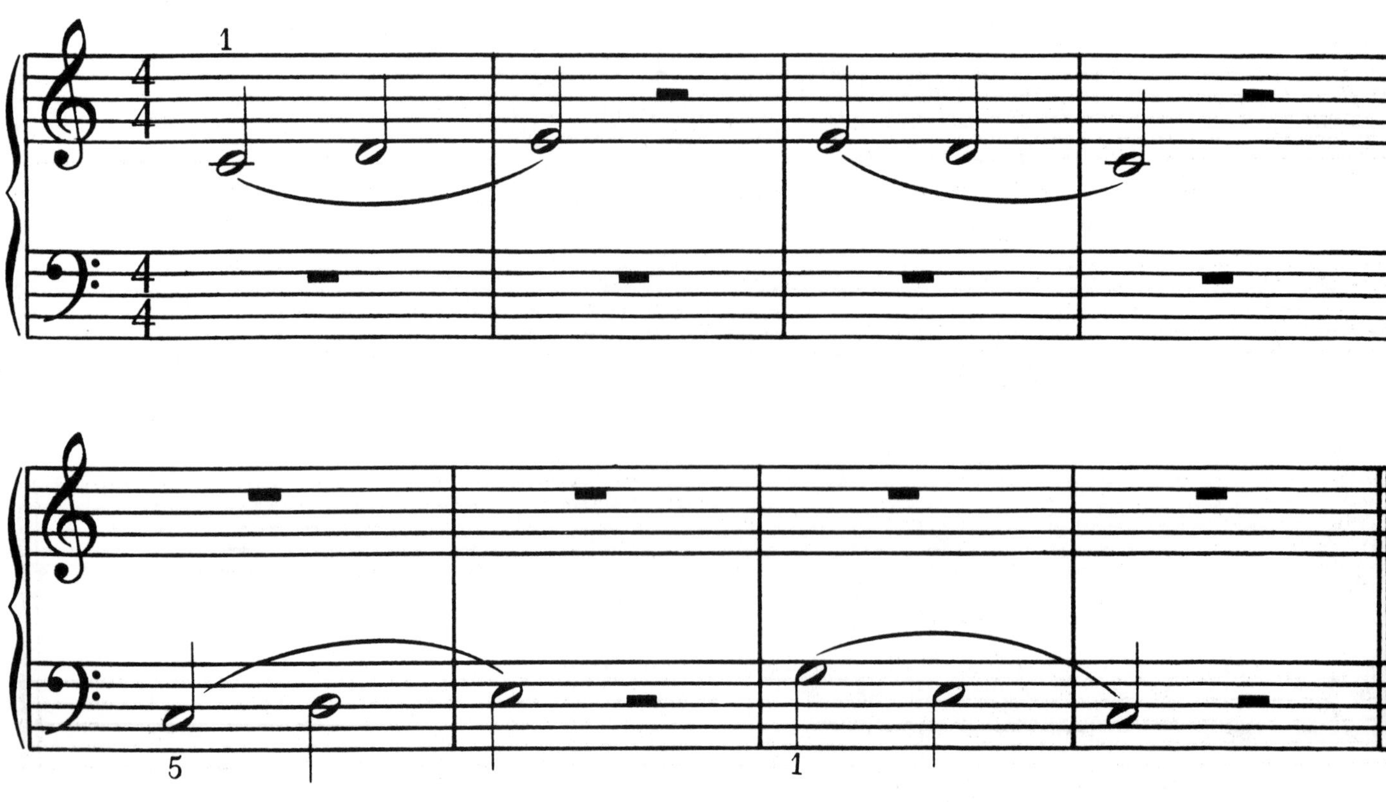

PLAYING 4THS

CHINESE DRAGON

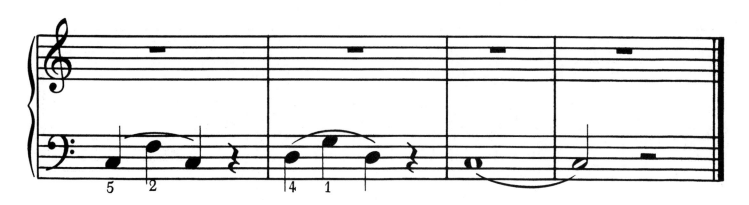

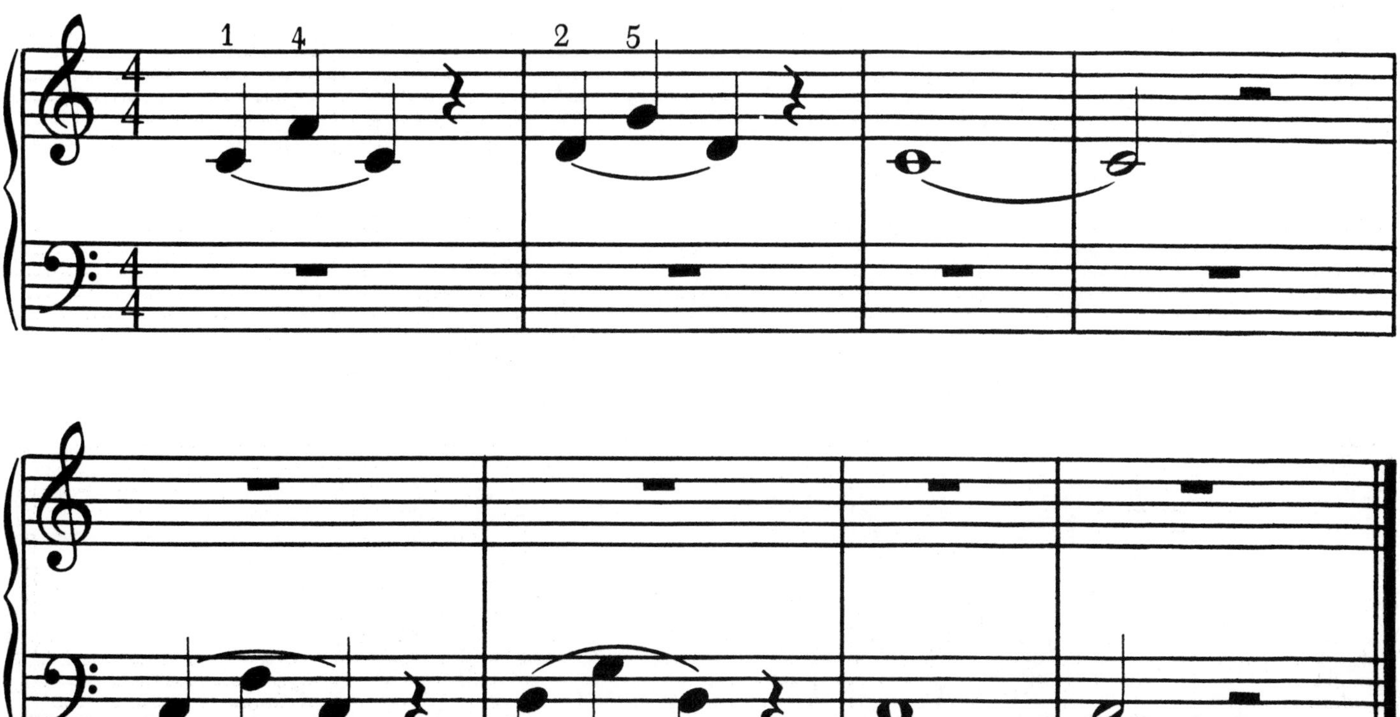
1 4
2 5
5 2
4 1

PLAYING 5THS

ROBBIE THE ROBOT

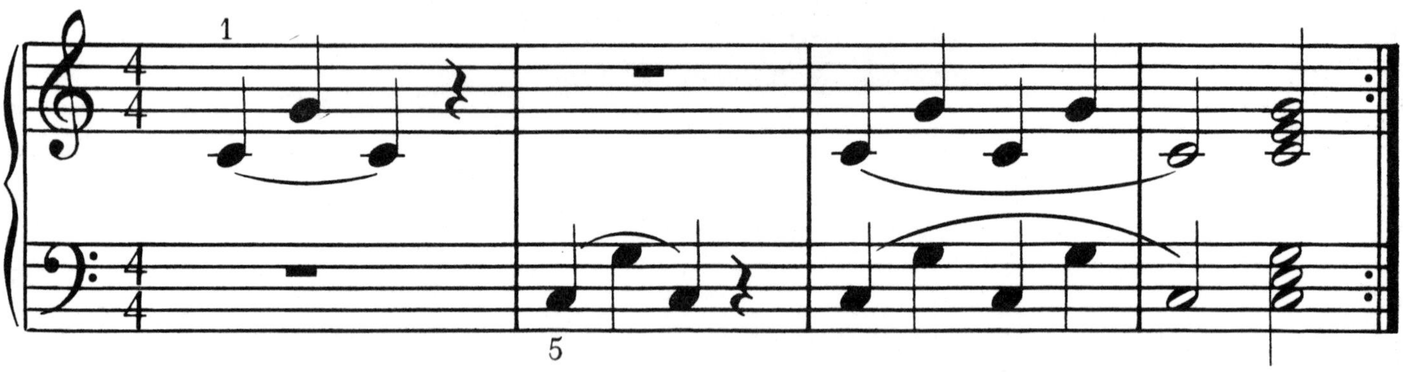

ROBERTA THE ROBOT

UNIT 6

MIDDLE C POSITION

WALKING HOME

f-p
1
5

RUNNING HOME

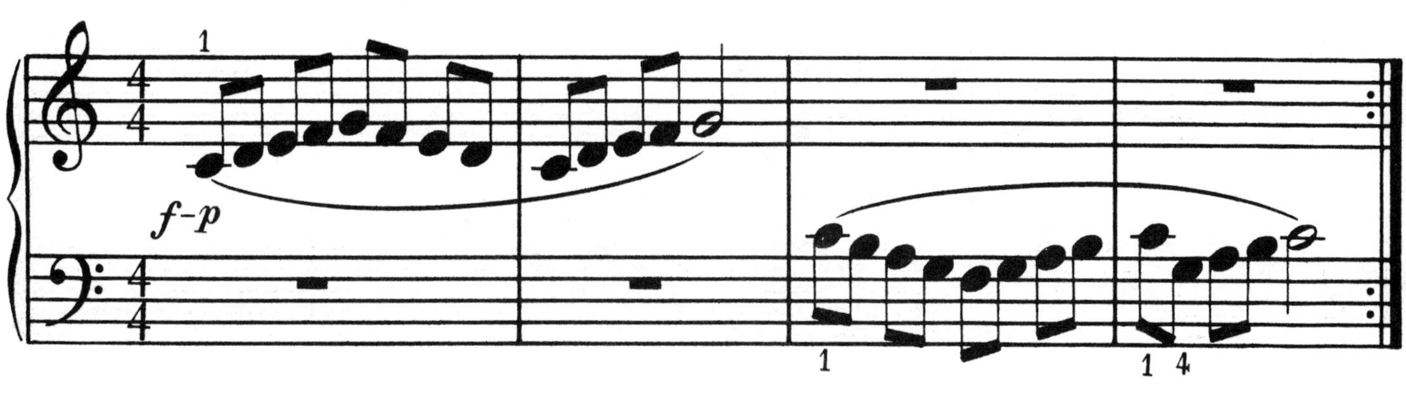
1
f-p
1
1 4

ROLLING A HOOP

f-p

SPINNING A TOP

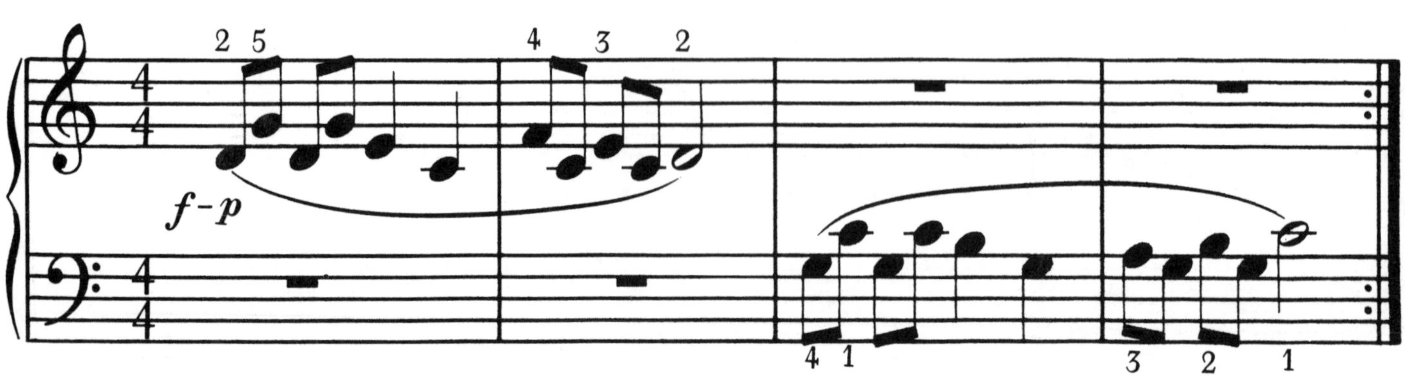
f-p

ROLLER COASTER RIDE

f–p

AIRPLANE RIDE

f–p

STACCATO

JUMPING ROPE WITH FRIENDS

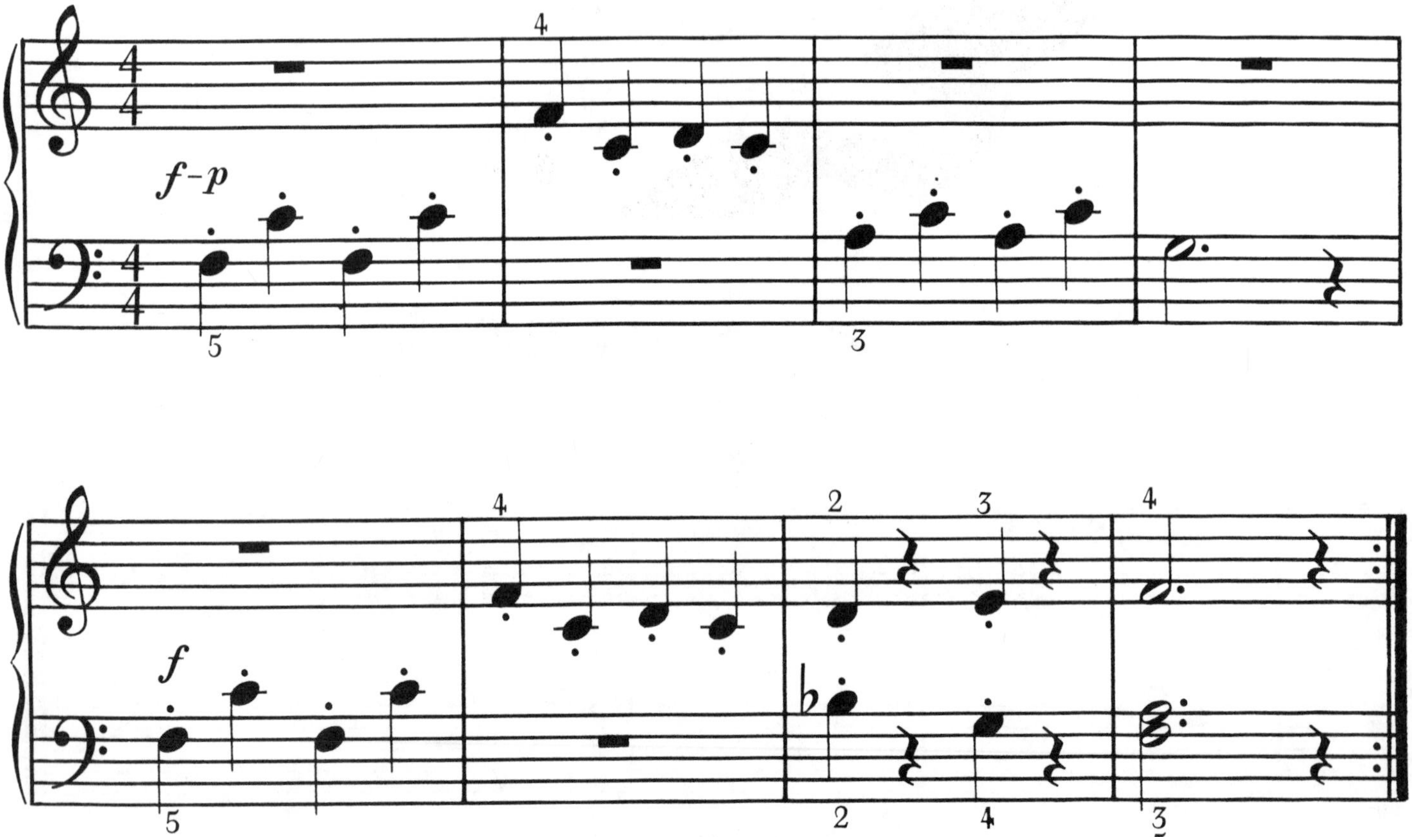
f–p
f

JUMPING ROPE ALONE

3
f–p
1

BOUNCING A BALL

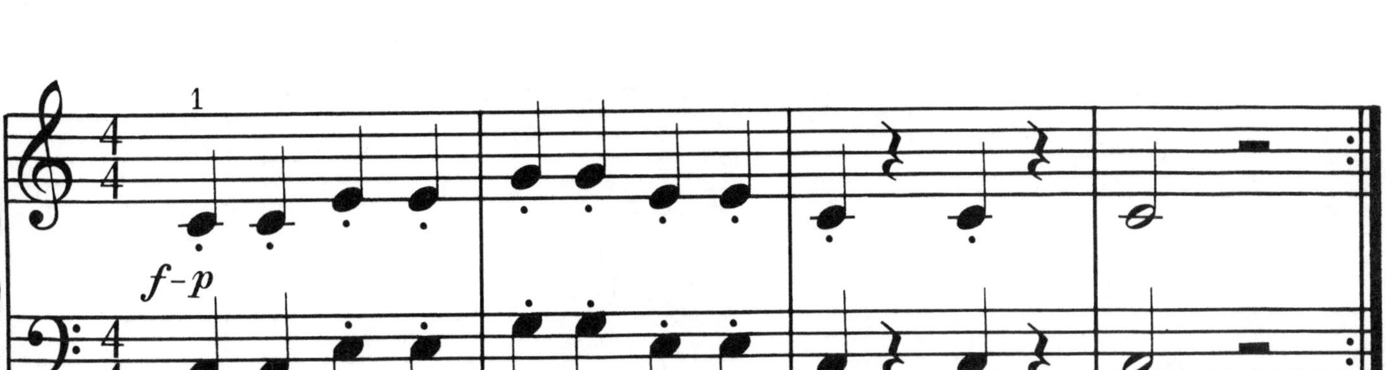
1
f–p
5

CHROMATIC PHRASE

SNAKE CRAWLING

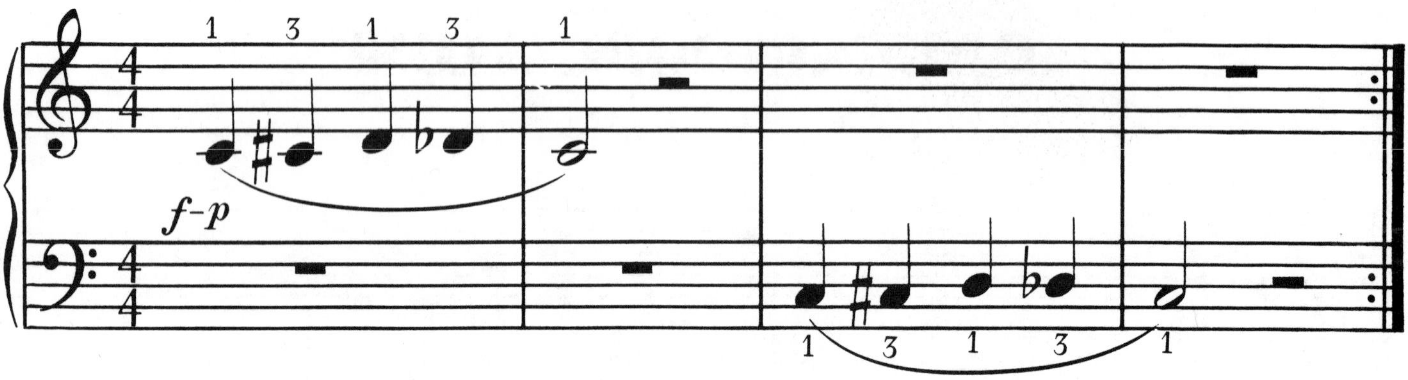
1 3 1 3 1
f-p
1 3 1 3 1

ARPEGGIO

TURNING CARTWHEELS

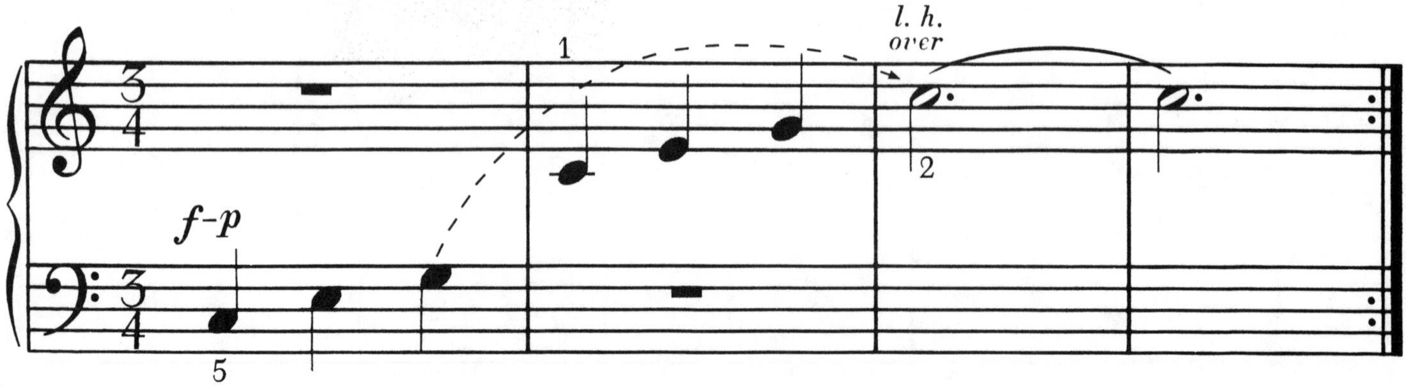
l. h.
over
1
2
f-p
5